The Author

David G.H. Crawford

Acknowledgement

I would like to thank my second wife Anne F. Crawford, for her assistance during my deliberations on this work. Although we are now divorced, we remain good friends and Anne has proven to be an excellent proof-reader of my preliminary draft work prior to having my book published.

Gravity

David G.H. Crawford

Matador
9 Priory Business Park,
Wistow Road, Kibworth Beauchamp,
Leicestershire. LE8 0RX
Tel: 0116 279 2299
Email: books@troubador.co.uk
Web: www.troubador.co.uk/matador
Twitter: @matadorbooks

ISBN 978 1838595 043

British Library Cataloguing in Publication Data.
A catalogue record for this book is available from the British Library.

Printed and bound by CPI Group (UK) Ltd, Croydon, CR0 4YY
Typeset in 10pt Helvetica Neue by Troubador Publishing Ltd, Leicester, UK

Matador is an imprint of Troubador Publishing Ltd

I dedicate this book to:

my son Steven Eric Crawford, currently residing in Beijing
my late wife (Gena) Geraldine Eugena Matthews Crawford
our late daughter Gena Kym Crawford (Mrs Chapman)

Contents

Preface

In my retirement, I have been drawn to reading various scientists' books and as a result, I have become aware of how quantum physics concepts have evolved, derived by people such as Neil Bohr, who developed Ernest Rutherford's theory of orbiting electron particles and Louie De Broglie who formulated the dual identity of particle and wave. Physics further developed with mathematical reasoning, by people such as Roger Feynman. Where the fundamental atom was initially believed to be as small as it gets, string theorists had derived ever smaller particles that make up the atom. Such theories, as well as being confirmed mathematically, appear to have been verified by experimental fragmentation work, carried out at CERN and other similar locations.

This is rather like some so-far undiscovered primitive tribesmen, in a South American jungle, finding a drone fallen from the sky. They would naturally have been bewildered as to how a strange sounding bird with one eye, no feathers or recognisable beak and, although now lifeless, had been able to fly with its 4 pairs of strange loose-hanging featherless wings. So, they had their tribal wise man investigate it. He devised ways by which he could "dismantle" more and more of it yet failed to understand how it had flown. Ultimately what parts he kept, he gave identities and stories, through which they became part of the tribal legends.

I fear this is what quantum physics has been doing with our fundamental atom, instead of recognising the hydrogen atom to be an **electromagnetic particle** borne from the Universe's majoritive

dark energy. I use the term "dark energy" since it is used to define what is now believed our Universe predominantly comprises of.

Before proceeding, perhaps I should establish an understanding of my integrity. With a Higher Maths credited HNC in Electrical Engineering, and broad operational experience originating in design application of electro-hydro rotating power-plant systems, and finally undertaking consultancy work in the water industry, I feel compelled to convey my personal theory on the Universe's fundamental energy structure and dare to believe that the scientific world should give it consideration.

If you feel my Personal Introduction, commencing on page xi, to be unnecessary, please go direct to **Introduction** *on page xxi.*

Personal Introduction

As my theory has developed over the past decade of my retirement years, and with my now lapsed membership of I. Eng. MIEIE, I decided on my eightieth birthday to sit a MENSA test in Nottingham, which I am pleased to say qualified me as a member of the High IQ Society. Thus, even in my late years, my reasoning is still intact.

You may ask, why I do not come straight to what my thesis "GRAVITY" has to say.

I most certainly would, if it were not for my recent experience of being turned down by a well-known science magazine. As I do not have an academic degree, I appeared to be prevented from having academia's magazine publication route take my theory on board. I therefore include this personal introduction, in which I provide anecdotes, hopefully to trigger the interest of one or two physicists where they may acknowledge my reasoning.

As a lad, formally invited to follow an academic route, but through impoverished family circumstances, declined the offer and chose to follow a three-year Scottish Junior Secondary educational path which ultimately lead to an immediate "modest earnings" trade-education route instead.

Clackmannanshire, where I grew up, is the smallest county in Scotland, located on the northern shores of the Firth of Forth and defined to the north by the Ochil Hills. Historically, before my time, several small townships thrived, along the foot of the Ochil Hill's southern slopes, each served by a burn (hill stream) with its own reservoir dam. The dams with their elevated levels, meant each community had their own hydro-electric turbine powered generated supply, to serve not just each community's needs, but also numerous industrial concerns, such as woollen textile mills, a paper mill, whisky distillation & malt-producing operations, collieries and of course farming, making Clackmannanshire and its county town of Alloa, very self-contained and prosperous back in the 1900s.

Alloa, built just off the Firth's northern shore's tidal mud flats, was a thriving industrial town, with breweries, glassworks and heavy engineering, which served not only its local industries but also the neighbouring county of Fife's Rosyth shipyard & Admiralty Docks. Close by, Fife's Longannet coal mine extended under the Firth where it had a vertical concrete shaft constructed up to a surface level above high tide allowing coal to be loaded directly onto sea-going vessels for exporting abroad.

I served my apprenticeship with what was then the world-famous manufacturer of rotating power-plant, the Harland Engineering Company in Alloa. The company is now history, long since absorbed into the Weirs Group. Harland manufactured turbines, pumps, motors, generators and alternators. I recall how we had many students from the Eastern & African countries and Central America, but particularly from India. The Indians, after experiencing their short spells in the factory's various workshops comprising a foundry, fabrication, lathe turning, armature winding, assembly fitting, and operational testing, on returning home, several retained what they learned and began locally to undertake pumping plant repairs. Perhaps that was an indication of how, the manufacturing industries the UK once had have ultimately moved East.

My five years apprenticeship included three years armature winding, followed by two years training as a rotating-plant test-technician. Armature winding was the electrical-circuitry installation part of the construction of rotating machines such as induction motors and motor-generator (M-G) sets. An M-G set such as illustrated on the following page's Figure A, incorporated a shaft mounted armature, with its integrally mounted and electrically wired, multi-segmented insulated copper commutator. The commutator was served by surrounding spring-loaded carbon brush-gear, through which the armature's generated alternating current was rectified and brought out to the machine's dc (direct current) terminal board.

Such equipment, classed as paper-gear, designed for the newspaper print processing industries, requiring both speed and voltage regulation tests, meant having to ensure that the brush-gear functioned, with minimal sparking across the gaps between the carbon brushes and the rotating segmented commutator. The sparks I recognised as transitional effects, resulting from "energy charge" diversion. As each of the rotating armature's energised commutator segments instantly vacated their peaked charge potential from the live brush-gear circuit, the brushes simultaneously served the oncoming segment's peaking potential, ensuring the machine output terminals to be at a constant dc voltage.

Should I be calling the aforementioned sparks, "electrons"? I think not!

The department carried out performance tests on all the company's manufactured rotating electrical and hydraulic plant. By tabulating speeds, mechanical, electrical and hydraulic instrumentation readings, load-curve characteristics were produced to verify that guaranteed design duties were being met. As the range of electrical power requirements was quite extensive, the department had at its disposal, various forms of ac and dc voltage supplies. The alternating current (ac) supplies were derived from a dedicated multi-tapped plug-board's transformer system and the dc supplies from a rotary convertor, all ultimately powered from a dedicated incomer fed from the National Grid.

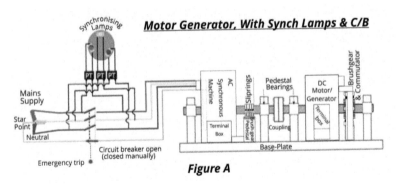

Figure A

To enable paper-gear speed-regulation testing, the company's rotary converter, as in Figure A, was a 3.3KV, 6 MW motor-generator (M-G) set. It comprised of a horizontally mounted, 3 phase 4 wire star-connected ac synchronous machine directly coupled to a dc machine. Each machine with its own field control meant that, whilst one was driven as a motor, the other would be a generator. Thus, we could have ac input and dc output, or vice-versa. The set was so massive, it permanently, took up 75% space of one end of the test-bed hall.

To test the paper-gear machines, it firstly, required the M-G set to be driven up from its dc end, to enable the ac end to be paralleled on to the main's incoming high-tension supply. This done, the ac end, as a synchronous motor, drove the dc end as a generator to supply the paper-gear's motor-generator sets, undergoing their voltage and speed regulation tests.

With reference to Figure A, paralleling onto the main supply required two people to engage the M-G set. One technician would manipulate the dc end as a motor, slowly bringing it up to speed. The other chap would monitor the ac end's voltage metering and control the alternator's excitation field in order to bring the generator phase voltages up to match the incomer main supply's level, both in frequency and potential.

As Figure A shows, the synchronising lamps connected via their potential transformers (PTs) across the open circuit breakers' up & down stream contactors were energised by whatever potential was across them. At standstill, the lamps circuitry would be continuously lit by the mains supply alone, continuity being brought through the mains & alternator's circuit breakers' star-points common neutral to complete the PTs' 3-phase circuitry, to the breaker's open terminals. As the alternator speed was brought up, the second operative manipulated the alternator's field current, to bring the 3 phase generated voltages up to equal the main supply, whilst observing the synchronising lamps.

Figure B illustrates how, when both supply and generated alternating 3 phase voltages were equal and in-step (synchronised), the voltage differences across the open circuit-breaker's terminals were zero. This meant the synchronous lamps had gone out, indicating it to be safe to close the circuit breaker.

However, synchronising is not quite like switching a light on or off. It requires very careful monitoring and adjustment of field control of volts and speed.

Figure C illustrates the M-G set's voltage variations that can arise. The Mains' 3 phase supply voltages red, yellow and blue, drawn as broken-lined waveforms, are shown to alternate from positive 3.3KV through zero to negative 3.3KV.

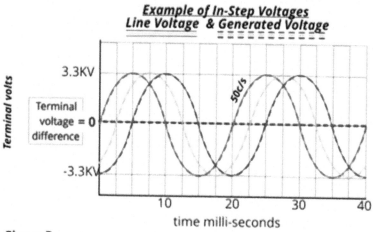

Figure B

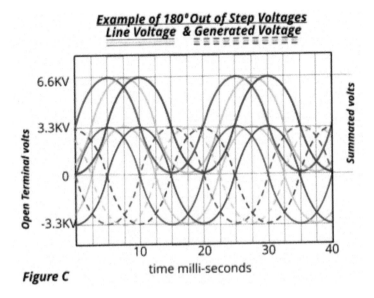

Figure C

time milli-seconds

The alternator's generated volts are shown to be 180 degrees out of step with the main supply. This means that unlike Figure B's equal in-step voltages' showing a constant zero difference across the terminals, Figure C shows how the M-G set's alternating voltages' zeros can intermittently coincide with the supply's zeros, yet be out of step by 180°. The result is that the summated red, yellow and blue waveforms show how 3.3KV- (-3.3KV) = 6.6KV, causes the potential transformers (PTs) energised synchronising lamps to be extremely bright with twice the phase voltages applied to the PTs.

By manipulating the speed of the M-G set to be generating at just less than 50c/s allowed synchrony to be located, where the phase displacement would slowly diminish, as would the lamps' brightness. This showed the generated voltages to be coming more in phase with the supply voltages. Thus, the instant the lamps went out was, as for Figure B, the perfect moment to close the circuit breaker, giving a smooth gentle paralleling of the M-G set on to the mains. At the same time the M-G set's dc end would have its field current switched off, ceasing its operation as a motor, and allowing the alternator to quietly run as a synchronous motor, ready to receive load from the dc end when acting as a generator, supplying the newly manufactured paper-gear sets trial tests.

The timing, in closing the circuit breaker, was of the essence. When correctly carried out, the process proves to be a straightforward procedure for experienced operators.

However, on my introduction to the operation, I had the "privilege" of manning the alternator end, whilst the experienced technician was bringing the dc end up towards the alternator's required synchronous speed. Where I prefer to think that the speed acceleration was a little too aggressive for the young lad's first attempt, one will never know. This much I do know! On just that one instance, I miss-timed closing the circuit-breaker, where instead of it "purring like a kitten", the machine went into violent "hunting" mode. Such *"is it a motor? is it a generator?"* conditions gave rise to the momentary in and out-of-phase voltages, causing high 6.6 KV spiking potentials and ferociously accelerating and decelerating speed fluctuations, with widely varying "starting" and "braking" torque levels.

The extreme speed accelerations and decelerations caused the air flowing in the machine's air-cooling core-passages to scream horrendously, whilst the highly torqued shaft caused the bearing housings to vibrate violently, shaking the test-bed hall's flooring and anyone standing on it! Within seconds, I recognised that the set could not be electrically "pulled in line" and immediately tripped the mains circuit-breaker, allowing the M-G set to free-wheel smoothly down towards stand-still.

You may ask:

"Is this relevant to matters of the Universe?"

It would seem perhaps not, other than, to experience such violence emanating from a great electro-mechanical rotating machine, gave validity to my youthful enquiring mind, pondering on such incredible violence. How could such power, derived from the invisible energy, transmitted through copper, iron, steel and air, in one moment, be smooth running, and then so electro-mechanically violent, the next?

The following evening, when attending further education classes for ONC electrical theory, the lecturer was presenting the Rutherford / Bohr concept of *orbiting electrons*. Having experienced what I have just related, I found there was no way I could believe that two powerful pulsating triple-phase energy potentials could be smoothly paralleled together, if anything like **"orbiting electrons"** were involved in the triple phase supplies. I just could not accept that electrons with today's concept of their "unpredictable" behaviour around protons could in any way play a part in machine synchronisation, pulsating energy yes, but not orbiting particles! For this reason, I have practised as an electrical engineer without needing to accept the *imaginary* orbiting particle concept.

Over the past decade, I have come to realise that professor JJ Thomson and his cathode ray tube (CRT) experiments, actually first spoke, of electrons as particles, which he believed were present in the energised gas he was using in the CRTs. Perhaps he as well as Rutherford, Bohr and De Broglie in their academic life were denied the possibility of experiencing such as what I have just described. Had they done so, I suspect that such experience, together, with their scientific knowledge in physics, would have taken them to less imaginative, more realistic routes in understanding the Universe.

On a lighter note, whilst serving two years conditional National Service, commencing as a 21 year old recruit in the RAF, I was trained over several months as an air radar mechanic in Bomber Command and soon became aware of the wonders of radio and radar transmission signalling. It proved to be totally different from that of 50c/s power transmissions. Whilst working in the station's radar test laboratory, when signal transmission tests on a frame-mounted rotating scanner were underway, one would be bathed in a "field" of radar signal transmissions. This meant one's body mass gradually acquired an induced electrostatic charge without being aware of it. If someone new to the premises walked in, still to build up their body's charge, it was a standard joke for someone to point a finger close to one of the unsuspecting newcomer's ears and see a "spark" jump across the "finger to ear" gap causing him a slight momentary discomfort. So, whether it is:

i.   a lightning bolt from the sky, striking a tree
ii. sparking across commutator brush-gear;
iii. the melting of a live cable's connector socket, when inadvertently "shorted" to earth;
iv. the playful "finger to ear" discharge in a radar lab,

I am very much aware of the infinite variations of electrostatic energy charge and discharge and its relationship to mass and space.

Thus, my career and service experience and current new-found interest in physics, brings me to declare how I regard electrons. **They are not particles, but measures of energy-exchange by discharge from high to low voltage levels**. Like photons, they are both forms of energy transients, photons of course, not electrostatic but electromagnetically induced transients. **There are no orbiting particles**. The only time "electrons" are seen, is when energy is being discharged through atoms in air-gaps, sometimes generating glowing heat, as sparks, where switchgear contactor's molten spots of metal are stretched to separation as upstream and downstream spring loaded contacts come apart, causing momentary transient charging of the atom filled air gap. Typical examples of energy transference are the sequentially controlled location points of energy discharge illuminating an oscilloscope or a **TV screen's high frequency, sequentially orientated, discharge points forming what appears as a moving black and white picture**.

Further discussion on this matter is given in the section titled "*The Dual Slot Baffle Transmission Chamber*".

Introduction

I hope the previous pages of personal experiential anecdotes has sustained your interest sufficiently to enable my extending it to the subject of **Gravity** and how I regard what is in effect the historic misconception of gravity.

Galileo brilliantly established how all objects of various mass, when released simultaneously from a great height, free of air drag, dropped to hit the earth at the exact same instant. Sir Isaac Newton, in his giving us the law of universal gravity, identified that no matter what it might be that was falling to Earth, if free of air-drag, it falls at an accelerating rate of 9.81 m/s^2. Einstein, in his general theory of relativity, spoke of spatial distortion of light beams and how force lines took the shape of "trampolines", as the reason for why we are all bound to Earth, yet neither he, Newton, or anyone else recognised what really causes gravity. In my taking to reading physics in my retirement, I am astounded by the extent that quantum physics has gone into identifying ever smaller increments of the fundamental atom to give us string theory. Yet still, there is no explanation for gravity!

I would much rather draw back from quantum physics & string theory, to the level of hydrogen atoms and their neutron cousins, where-in, I believe lies the source of gravity.

My reasoning, although, having evolved from the non-academic industrial trade route career, is very much theoretically orientated. I spent many years travelling, investigating and advising on problems concerning the operation of electromagnetic powered, water supply and waste-water processing systems. What with my RAF radar experience, and a period in application engineering in air-conditioning and refrigeration-storage systems, this meant my developing a thorough understanding of:

i. Consequential voltage drops.
ii. Loss of hydrostatic pressure heads due to air entrapment.
iii. Centrifugally generated water pressures.
iv. Loss of pressure head due to cavitation at pump suction bell-mouth.
v. Temperature control in positive displacement liquid to gas refrigeration plant.
vi. Vibrational fracturing and coupled shafts misalignments.
vii. Excessive temperature increase in electrical driven pump-sets, resulting from one of the various failures, such as a burst rising main, a seized motor or pump bearing or shaft mis-alignment.
viii. Deterioration in metals, etc., to name but a few.

I find with my years of troubleshooting in plant-operation in mine-dewatering, water-distribution, wastewater-processing, air-conditioning and cold-storage meant my dealing with most parameters of energy fault-finding in engineering. Such experience enables me to look back, past the historically profound theories in electromagnetic engineering's rotating field's *dual "**positive and negative**" terminology.*
I recognise that fundamental electrostatic monopole energy must be the dark energy the scientific world is now theorising over.
As I said previously, I tried to communicate with the scientific world by offering my theory to a recognised leading science magazine. They declined my offer, advising that the magazine was produced for academics by academics. They advised they would pass my theory around their sub-editors where someone might get

back to me. That was several years ago with no response.

I have since become acquainted with Dr Ron Evans, the retired aerospace engineer, known for his book, titled "Greenglow" and the subsequent Horizon documentary titled "Greenglow – The Quest for Gravity Control".

After a lengthy telephone conversation, when I mentioned the negative response I had received from the magazine publisher, he recommended that, before divulging my theory to him or anyone else, I should have a book published on it.

Ron referred me to Sandy Kidd, a retired North Sea Oil official, who also served National Service as an air radar technician in Bomber Command.

Sandy, when servicing one of the bombers' air radar system, he had personal experience of being thrown off balance as he descended the bomber's radom access-ladder, due to the gyro he had just removed and was carrying in his pocket to take back to the test laboratory. Whilst he came to no harm, the fact that such a small device, still literally spinning within its framed structure, could distort his body's balance-alignment to gravity inspired his curiosity.

In his later years, as well as appearing on television, assisting Professor Eric Laithwaite (now deceased), with his gravity defying shaft mounted rotating wheel demonstrations, he dedicated much of his spare time to developing a gravity-defying dual gyroscopic structure. Somehow, local academics, on investigating his work, failed to support his efforts in trying to have his design adopted by industrial entrepreneurs. Perhaps what I have got to say may cause them to re-visit Sandy.

Both Ron and Sandy made me aware of just how many free-thinking individuals there are throughout the world who have dedicated their private time and money to devise ways of overcoming gravity. None, however, recognise the historic misconception of gravity that humanity has been living with. Perhaps, if my theory is recognised, the scientific world will re-align the direction of their research. After several communications with both gentlemen, I decided to put my theory into print.

Dark Energy

Fundamental Electrostatic Energy

I believe **dark energy** to comprise of infinite numbers of fundamental *monopole points of electrostatic charge,* all of positive value. Consequently, they repulse each other, to a greater or lesser extent, depending on their locational surroundings. The value of the charge is so small that it is undetectable to the human senses, and *I assume it to be equal to that of the mean value of a pulsating hydrogen proton.*

Figure 1 illustrates how I visualise an electrostatic charged energy point. It spherically extends its energy field outward, through infinite numbers of flux field lines, each normal to the field's figurative tangent. *I say figurative,* since the field lines, although radially equal in potential, do not physically make a sphere and will fill space cubically, field lines, varying in length and respective charge as per its surrounding limits.

For the purpose of moving the discussion forward, I show the fundamental point and its energy field as a spherical image. The cubic space it actually occupies will be discussed later. The charge's energy level, a maximum at its central

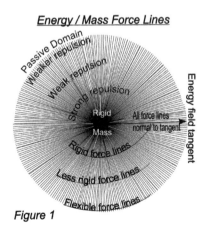

Energy / Mass Force Lines

Figure 1

point, diminishes by the square of the inverse of the field's radius increase. Therefore, in its expansion, the field's positive repulsion varies in strength from strong, to weak, to passive. *The flux (field) lines, being totally rigid at and around the central point, form fundamental mass.* The field lines gradually, if unrestricted, lose their rigidity in proportion to their repulsive charge. They become flexible beyond a given extended radius to ultimately become passive.

The Universe is currently understood to comprise of 95.1% dark energy/mass, which I assume to be a spherically **boundless dark energy ocean (BDEO)** of energy points. To ensure there is no misunderstanding regarding mass and energy, where Einstein gave us $e=mC^2$, I prefer to recognise that energy is mass wherever the force lines form rigidly, be it around each point's centre or in the complex element-structures, of which we and all else are comprised. Therefore, where I state the BDEO to be 95.1% of the Universe, I choose not to separate the 95.1 % into an energy and mass ratio. For the purpose of this book, when I say energy, I am including for mass, if it is relevant.

Figure 1a represents a minutely small region of the BDEO. For the purpose of illustration, I show one of the electrostatic energy points drawn large with hollow arrow heads to indicate how all of the BDEO points' fields form an ocean of passive charge. This means they all peacefully coexist, each occupying their own domain, subject to their neighbourhood's status.

Part of Universe's Boundless Dark Ocean (BDEO)

Figure 1a

Fundamental Energy Point (FEP)

In advancing the discussion, I have redrawn the energy point as in Figure 2, which I now call, a **Fundamental Energy Point (FEP)** shown with its energy field's spherical reference levels, drawn two-dimensionally, as circles. *It also shows how the FEP becomes a **passive FEP (pFEP)** as it converges on the BDEO.*

Fundamental Energy Point (FEP)

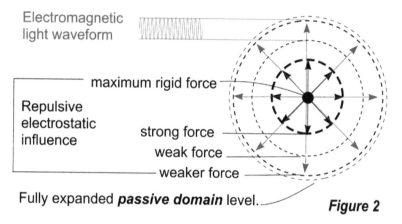

Figure 2

Note how, although the FEP is electrostatic, its extended field at weak to passive levels is shown to carry pulsating light waves. These result from inductive transmission, occurring around each point, from intersecting energy charge levels, of its immediate neighbouring FEPs' fields. The light, therefore, travelling instantly, by induction, spreads radially, as if in waves and consequently by chain reaction, "appears" to be travelling as straight light beams. It would explain Einstein's theory of starlight beams appearing to bend around the sun. This topic is discussed in greater detail in the section titled "Starlight".

In Figure 2 it will be noted how, where one normally draws sine waves with maximum level equal to highest potential, in this instance

I am showing sine-waves drawn inversely, where maximum force level is at the centre point of the diagram and the lowest level (non-repulsive passive domain) at an outer radius. The light-radiating waves pulsate in the passive domain levels, where it in no way influences the repulsive domain's electrostatic energy charge levels.

The term "wave", whilst used, of course represents the field line radii values, which radiate respectfully throughout 360 degrees, with the energy from each centre point to their field's passive regions. These regions in their passivity intersect their neighbouring fields' passive domains, as stated above, enabling the inductive transmission of all light and ultra-light energy waves across the heavens.

This topic, however, deserving much more discussion, is best left to another day!

My concern at the moment relates to **universal integral repulsion,** and how it affects FEP neighbourhoods and regions. Figure 3 shows a transparent three-dimensional view of a *Fundamental Group of Thirteen FEP's* spherically arranged force fields. Each is drawn as a transparent sphere, relating territorially to its immediate neighbours.

Fundamental Group of Thirteen FEPs

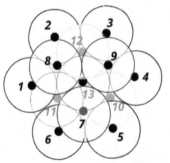

Figure 3

The numbered "13" FEP can be seen to be central to twelve surrounding FEPs which, although not shown, could be either all pFEPs or FEPs, or graduations of both, depending on where they are located. Where they are FEPs, they would be in repulsion, all trying to expand away from each other.

Groups of 13, of course, do not exist alone and are each one of infinite numbers of groups that go into making up the BDEO. Thus, every FEP or pFEP can be both an inner 13th as well as simultaneously being one of twelve surrounding FEPs, to not one, but to twelve other groups. This identical structural relationship, as will soon be seen, gives rise to a *network of instantaneous force lines.*

Structure of the Universe

Where I described the BDEO as being boundless, and populated by pFEPs, that was not entirely true. Possibly, due to either a Big Bang or the presence of many Black Holes, there is at least one **internal dark sea (IDS)** as shown in Figure 3a.

The BDEO, being so infinitely vast, means there could be other IDSs so far away from us that our astronomers as yet are unaware that there are vast regions of BDEO between them and our IDS.

Unlike the BDEO's totally passive pFEP population, the IDS's FEPs vary from passive expansion, at its outer peripheral region to gradually diminish in field volume, where their nuclei become greatly condensed to their near maximum charge. The IDS's centrally compressed spherical region, estimated to be 4.9% of the Universe, wherein you, I and all that we see reside, I shall call **Our Part** of the **Universe (OPU).**

The IDS's graduated states of FEP expansions are partially illustrated in Figure 3b. The BDEO's pFEPs, shown in blue, are a segmental part of their

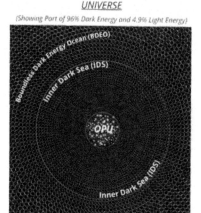

UNIVERSE
(Showing Part of 96% Dark Energy and 4.9% Light Energy)

Boundless Dark Energy Ocean (BDEO)

Inner Dark Sea (IDS)

OPU

Inner Dark Sea (IDS)

Figure 3a

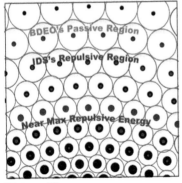

Neighbourhood of FEPs
Showing Variations in Parameters

BDEO's Passive Region

JDS's Repulsive Region

Near Max Repulsive Energy

Figure 3b

complete peripheral surrounding of the inner graduated FEPs. Field volumes, all diminishing in size, have a simultaneous increase in their points' charge and mass.

The question has to be, *"Why are they in graduated states of expansion/compression?"*

The currently believed Big Bang is estimated to have occurred 13.9 billion years ago, emanating from an infinitesimally small point of unimaginably high energy, exploding into an infinite number of expanding energy cells or points. *I haven't been able to understand how anything so small yet powerful could come to be.* With that said, I prefer not to dwell on "how it all began" but to view the now established existence of Black Holes.

I regard Black Holes to be the Universe's re-cycling process of the OPU and give my thoughts on this subject later in the section tilted "Black Hole".

Keeping in mind that energy cannot be destroyed but transformed, the extreme form of transformation has to be a Black Hole's dismantling of active and burnt out stars and reducing them to fundamental electrostatic energy/mass particles, i.e. the FEPs. Perhaps the equivalent of a Big Bang output occurred as a result of all Black Holes converging to be as one. *This would mean of course there never was a moment when only one energy point existed!* To comprehend how such transformations come about, we must first understand the interaction between groups of FEPs and how so many of them become electromagnetic particles.

So, having recognised the variation in FEPs, how do they transform from their dark energy/mass into the electromagnetic energy/mass of the OPU?

To answer this, let's explore how FEPs' force fields relate to their neighbours and neighbourhoods.

Field Force Lines

As Figure 3 showed, each FEP is surrounded by twelve neighbours, where each has twelve points of tangential contacts. Two dimensionally, that shows as six points of tangential contacts, as in Figure 4. It can be seen how, where what are infinite numbers of *field force lines (FFLs)*, six equally spaced FFLs are shown enhanced by enlarged symbolic arrow heads as a repulsive star formation.

Thus, with the star formation being common to each and every FEP, groups of seven FEPs (thirteen, three dimensionally) form networks of tangential FFLs, as shown in Figure 4a. These networks exist throughout the entire

FEP
Field Force Lines (FFLs)

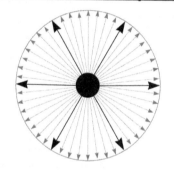

Figure 4

Tangentially Related Field Force Lines (FFLs)

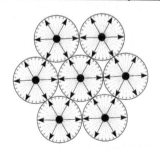

Figure 4a

passive BDEO as well as in the electrostatic graduated field regions of the IDS. The spherical IDS is in a state of infinite variation. Its electrostatic FEP fields range from a minimum volume at maximum charge, in the central region, to an expanded volume of passive charge at its peripheral boundary with the BDEO.

It should be noted that where the force line networks are represented by arrowheads, this does not mean that the arrowheads have values that would cancel each pair out. They symbolically represent electrostatic charges, which transform into higher or lower levels, subject to the measure of locational field expansion or compression in their groups and networks. It follows, therefore, that the FEP field volumes vary relative to their monopole repulsion charge. The variation of course is in accordance with the inverse change in field radius squared, all subject to their surrounding neighbours and location. I once again emphasise, in no way do they cancel each other out.

Local Force Lines

We must now consider the extrapolation of these pairs of FFLs, where in FEP clusters they form relative **Local force lines (LFLs),** as shown in Figure 4b. Note how, unlike their pairs of FFLs, they take the form of singular lines, with each end having an arrowhead. In the case of Figure 4b's group, each LFL extends over three FFLs, i.e. 1&1/2 FEPs, where one end

Local Force Lines (LFLs)

Figure 4b

points outward, and the other inward to the middle of the central FEP. There it meets its inline, equal and opposite pointing partner. The LFLs form star formation structures just as the FEP's singular FFLs do. Also, where each double arrowhead line is extended over three single arrow headed lines, this does not mean it represents a value of one and a half charges. It represents the force of two charges, just as the five others (eleven, three dimensionally) do, which emanate from the central FEP.

FEPs' Electrostatic Local Force Lines Networks

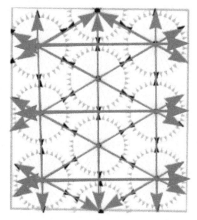

Figure 4c

With reference to Figures 1 and 2, where they show the forces lines to define every direction of the 360° surrounding each FEP, this means that no matter where the FEP is located, its energy force lines emanate from its central point, relating to its neighbours' equivalent force lines. Figure 4c illustrates how any structural activity that may exist anywhere within the IDS, networks of LFLs will form. Note how LFLs are shown extended vertically and horizontally as well as diagonally across the FEPs.

Such networks extend throughout the IDS's fabric of force lines, where no matter what occurs anywhere in the IDS, force reactions will be accommodated throughout the networks relative to their location. To emphasise this, I show the following two figures.

Figure 4ci is an example of how FFLs form neighbourhoods of local networks which, as well as summating to have resultant

LFLs, you will note how the networks coincide with other networks, where LFLs cross over each other, sharing the same parallelogram of FFLs.

Figure 4cii illustrates how, over larger regions of the IDS, the network's inter-relationships remain true, but in larger and in more comprehensive configurations.

Where the network structures look similar to those of Figure 4ci, Figure 4cii networks embrace greater numbers of FFLs where each network is defined by LFLs. For the purpose of illustration, I show six with their LFLs also illustrated, two pairs of which overlap as a result of the three overall resultant LFLs crossing over each other. I trust this emphasises the integration that exists throughout the parallelogram formations of LFL defined FFL networks.

FFL Neighbourhood Networks

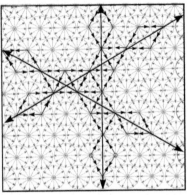

Figure 4ci

Larger Regions' LFL Networks

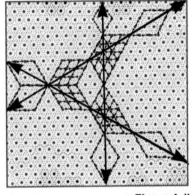

Figure 4cii

Ultimately, every tangential LFL formation relates to all of the Universe's electrostatic dark energy's non-passive networks. In effect, all energy forces act instantly, be it spatial, light or radio-wave.

Major Force Lines

Where the FFLs were shown to accumulate into LFLs, so too do the LFLs align to form into *Major Force Lines (MFLs)* and combinations of both MFLs and LFLs. As shown in Figure 4d, these extend all the way out with the OPU's periphery to the IDS, where their outward pointing arrowheads are shown as white to indicate the status of passivity. Similarly, their arrowheads that point inwards are black, indicating maximum charge level, or increasing towards maximum charge level when aligned with dedicated LFLs, or LFL clusters. Consequently, an aligned LFL defining the IDS's central zone has an inward pointing black arrowhead, confirming the increasing to maximum charge.

As stated previously, just as each FEP, subject to balanced conditions, have equal and opposite pairs of FFLs, each pair representing the diameter of the FEP, so too does the IDS have theoretically, pairs of equal and opposite MFLs spanning the IDS, as shown horizontally and diagonally in Figure 4d. I use the word theoretically since, in actuality, as

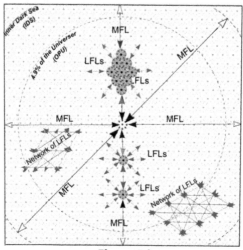

Figure 4d

mentioned above, combinations of MFLs and LFLs form aligned pairs to predominantly represent the balanced radii of the IDS, as shown vertically in Figure 4d. Although only a few alignments are shown, the counterbalance of all pairs of MFLs and of combinations of LFLs and MFLs exist throughout 360 degrees around the centre of the IDS and its OPU. It is hoped that the very approximate diagram sufficiently conveys what actually is occurring throughout the infinite numbers of FEPs populating the IDS. Clearly, networks of LFLs exist throughout the IDS, samples of which are shown in Figure 4d.

It is through such networks, that it will be understood both gravity and light transmission exists in our part of the Universe.

Figure 4e shows how the MFLs tend to define the IDS, out-with the OPU's 4.9% part of the Universe. Within the OPU, the figure illustrates it to be a region populated by neighbourhoods of separate masses which can be seen to relate to the central region, with LFLs playing their subordinate alignment roles to the MFLs. Each mass of energy points are, of course, defined not only by the aligned MFL and LFL pairs, but also by additional concentrically arranged clusters of LFLs, as shown in Figure 4d.

In short, therefore, Figure 4e illustrates how the continuously formed MFLs predominantly occupying the IDS out-with the OPU, relying on the LFL networks to maintain the centralised balance that the MFLs require to equate to the peaceful balance of the BDEO's passivity.

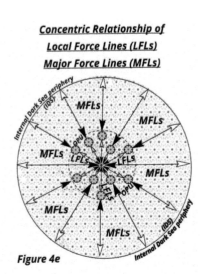

Concentric Relationship of Local Force Lines (LFLs) Major Force Lines (MFLs)

Figure 4e

The FEP formations shaded grey are drawn to show how, where they reside at various distances from the OPU's central zone, their electrostatic force fields are subject to widely varying levels of compression. As already established, the nearer they are to the centre of the OPU, the greater their energy points' charges are, with their fields more compressed.

It follows that because of the increasing levels of compression, the electrostatic FEPs cannot remain static. Their repulsive charge becomes so strong that they begin to jiggle and jive. Such activity spreads throughout the OPU.

**So what results from the jiggling and jiving? One may ask!
Dark Energy transforms into Light Energy.**

Light Energy

Pulsating Energy Points

Figure 5 shows both the spherical and cubic field reference lines illustrated three-dimensionally, enabling the reader to see how the instability must have come about. Where the tangentially normal black force lines show their spherical alignment, it is clear that the force lines are redder in colour, as they comply with the volumetric cubic parameters. One can see the longer and lighter red the force lines are, the more misaligned they are with those of their neighbours.

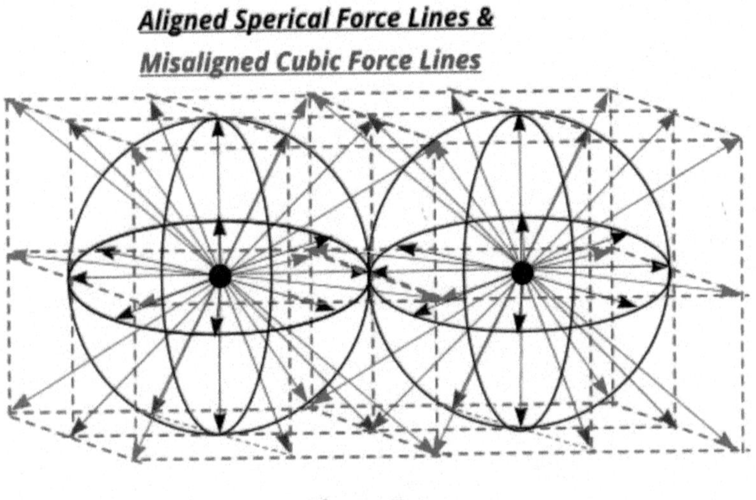

Aligned Sperical Force Lines & Misaligned Cubic Force Lines

Figure 5

14

Partial erratic spin zones shown in red
for PEPs subjected to extreme
compression & related cubic volumes

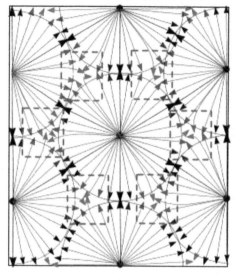

Figure 5a

Figure 5a is a sectional view of grouped **pulsating energy points (PEPs)**, with their central one (the numbered 13 in Figure 3) with six of the twelve chaotic zones (coloured red) indicating the misalignment of the extended red force lines. Where Figure 5 showed the misaligning red lines the instant before the turbulence occurs, Figure 5a shows the instant after turbulence occurs.

Rather than oppose their neighbouring counterpart, the red force lines submit, by buckling in such a way as to unite with its misaligned neighbours, to create non-defined directional partial spinning torque. Such transience gives rise to erratic repulsive behaviour, showing how the PEP fields must begin to jiggle and jive, causing the tangential alignments to cease. Each and every PEP centralised, in conflict, with its twelve surrounding neighbours, has the same problem, giving rise to chaotic turbulence.

Hydrogen Atom

Such chaotic activity must transform the FEPs into PEPs, whose fields became electromagnetic. As electromagnetic effects built up with increased frequency, the nucleus of each PEP must have increased in mass size to gradually develop into a pulsating proton. As the frequency drew nearer to 1450MHz, the PEP transformed into the fundamental *Hydrogen atom*. By virtue of how they came into being, the H atoms' chaotic repulsive behaviour would have lessened, as the PEPs unstable neighbourhoods transformed into synchronising spiralling clouds of Hydrogen.

The comparison between an H atom and its original FEP format is illustrated in Figure 5b. The energy pulsations result in the central point taking on the identity of the proton. Such a situation, where an FEP and an H atom reside side by side, cannot arise, of course,

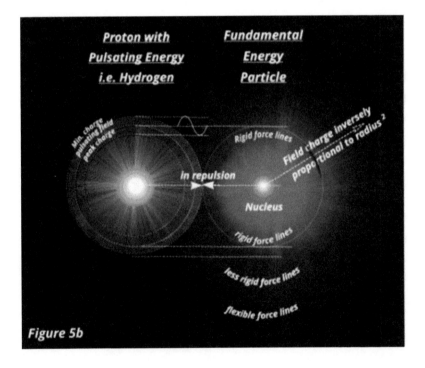

Figure 5b

Universal Expansion/Compression

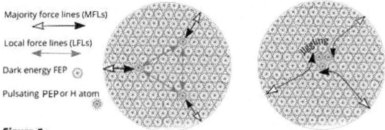

Majority force lines (MFLs)

Local force lines (LFLs)

Dark energy FEP

Pulsating PEP or H atom

Figure 5c

since the energy pulsations of one cell or atom must instantly affect the stability of its neighbours.

Where one might ponder on how hydrogen clouds are formed, Figure 5c shows how three PEPs in their jiggling and jiving, separated by LFLs, begin to undulate in a resonant fashion, where they transform into pulsating H atoms. Their resonance brings them together when the grey LFLs merge with the MFLs. Combined, the H atoms' resonance amounts to their synchronising into mutual spinning, where more and more atoms accumulate into forming hydrogen gas clouds. As the spiralling H atom clouds became so vast, their vortices formed into heat generating stars.

Referring to Figure 4e, in which I mentioned the variation in electrostatic compression was subject to the location of the PEPs. The closer to the centre of the OPU, the stronger and more rigid their fields' lines are, where they soon transform into H atoms. The further from the centre of the OPU, however, means the slight lessening of compression, with longer and less rigid field force lines submitting to greater distortion. No longer jiggling and jiving, they commit to spinning in definite rotations, where their fields extend extensively.

It is clear at this stage that I prefer to regard the proton as a whole entity without looking to break it down into smaller particles.

From Figure 5b, the proton is shown to be a derivative of an FEP's nucleus, whose field, now pulsating, causes an induced

Formation of Neutron

1/6
FEP with MFLs
surrounding it.

2/6
FEP transforms into
a pulsating FEP, ie PEP

3/6
PEP transforms into H atom
but nucleus spinning
causes excessive field expansion
to buckle fied lines

4/6
spinning slows down
when force lines double
back on themselves towards
nullifying nucleus

5/6
Spinning stop when totally double
backed field lines merge into
enlarging nullified nucleus

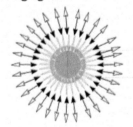

6/6
Neutron
still has
MFLs
acting on it

Figure 5d

reinforcement to the nucleus point's mass, transforming it into the proton. Similarly, with turbulence occurring at regions where field expansion is more excessive, I believe neutrons to be the protons, whose field lines have undergone a neutralising process such as I show in Figure 5d's six stages. Please view each of the six stages in sequence to grasp the process I am proposing.

Combining of Hydrogen Atoms

Returning once more to the hydrogen atom, let's visualise an instant where two H atoms are momentarily held together with MFLs.

What would that be like?

Figure 5e illustrates the situation, two dimensionally, where MFLs totally encompass a pair of H atoms. The MFLs, each a summation of all the force line network structures, clearly overpowers the atoms' internal force lines to push the atoms together, so much so that the

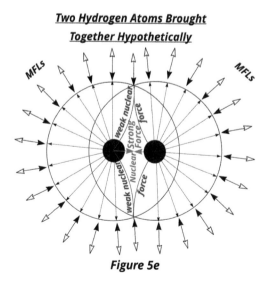

Figure 5e

directly opposing atom force-lines, drawn in red, are shown two-dimensionally, as to how a combined three-dimensional diaphragm of entrapped distorted energy lines (nuclear force) is formed. Its core's centrally opposing field lines are of a proportion of twice the inverse of each atom field's radius-increase squared.

For this reason, hydrogen atoms cannot reside together. The opposing excess force lines are unable to remain aligned and must relent by creating locational displacement spins on the atoms, giving rise to the hydrogen cloud formations.

But then there is something missing here!
What is missing, of course, are the Neutrons!

For all H atoms perfected, equal amounts of neutrons evolving is envisaged. With their nullified energy status, the MFLs nudge them towards entrapment between the hydrogen atoms. Where one neutron between two hydrogen atoms would soon be displaced by the H pulsating fields and MFLs, two neutrons appease the MFLs by pairing up between two H atoms becoming entrapped by the distorted nuclear force lines.

Figure 5f shows a Helium atom's two entrapped neutrons. Their presence causes the intermediate field force lines to distort in a less chaotic manner, allowing synchronising undulations to occur. The heavier the elements become, with more and more neutrons distorting the atoms' force fields that entrap them, this surely gives rise to generating the ultra-high frequencied rhythmic characteristic from which **Nuclear Energy's strong to weak radio-active forces accumulate**? This much is for certain, the coming together of hydrogen to give us all the other elements most certainly needs neutrons to modulate what would otherwise be chaotic direct in-line opposing forces. Neutrons could well have played a part in stabilising the hydrogen activity into forming their spiralling clouds! Be that as it may!

Two H Atoms Brought Together With Two Neutrons = Helium
(Showing field line distortion ie Nuclear Energy)

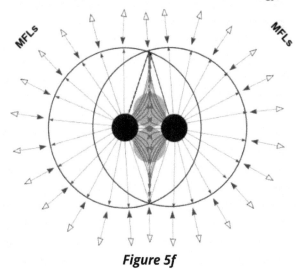

Figure 5f

Together with MFLs, they play the major role of uniting hydrogen atoms to form all the other elements, without the need for Neil Bohr's imaginative orbiting electrons.

Neutron Dragged Major Force Lines (ndMFLs)

Rather than discuss the formation of the elements, I choose to stay with the phenomenal role neutrons play in calming our OPU part of the Universe.

So far, I have defined FFLs, LFLs and MFLs, and explained how all the LFLs merge into pairs of opposing MFL/LFL groups. The combination of MFLs and LFLs form the network balance that must prevail, throughout the IDS region. The OPU's PEP population, however, has transformed into hydrogen gas clouds with star forming vortices. As already noted, the process nullified large numbers of would-be hydrogen atoms into becoming neutrons, which combined with the unspoiled hydrogen to form the other elements.

Neutron-dragged MFL (ndMFL)

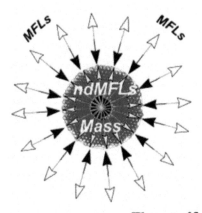

Figure 4f

Because of its neutron content, the element-formed mass's structured local force lines, are weaker than LFLs and are unable to merge with them or the MFLs. Thus, these weaker local force lines, instead of calling them LFLs, I call them *neutron dragged MFLs (ndMFLs)*. Figure 4f illustrates an ndMFL mass surrounded by MFLs which, whilst not being able to absorb the mass's ndMFLs, maintains a compressive force around them, holding them all together. Note: **together without the need for the imaginative "orbiting electrons".**

Neutron Dragged OPU

Figure 4g illustrates a sample of four blue ndMFL clusters, contained within the central OPU region, each surrounded by MFLs & LFLs. This new variation of main force lines exists in all body mass as well as in non-solid gaseous elements, excluding hydrogen, throughout the OPU. This means that where the IDS's MFLs continue to merge with all in-line LFLs, including those in neutron-free H atoms, they fail to merge with all the neutron dragged mass ndMFLs. Whilst it is not obvious at this point, hopefully the time taken, to show how fundamental force lines are the fabric of both the electrostatic and electromagnetic structure of our OPU, will be justified with what I am about to convey.

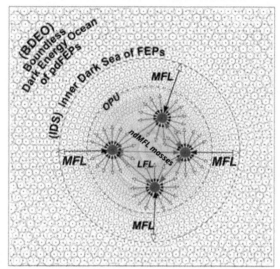

Figure 4g

Gravity

By identifying the ndMFLs, I am, figuratively speaking, shining a light on the ultimate mystery that has evaded Newton and just evaded Einstein in his devising of the "bending gravity trampoline" & bowed light theories. I am of course referring to **Concentric Gravity.**

Every individually separate atom containing neutrons is subject to concentric gravity, just as all atom combinations are.

Where two bodies in space come close together, providing their rates of displacement (speed) in space is negligible, the MFLs will push them together. This is how our Earth and all other planets formed, from exploded star debris, being pushed together. I am, in effect, describing the **gravitational force network** that concentrically exists around every individual body or mass, whether it is a star, a planet, a galaxy, you, I, or Isaac Newton's apple. It, they, we, are all separate neutron dragged masses, subject to the Universal IDS's concentric energy differential between the dark electrostatic network of MFLs and the OPU's neutron dragged electromagnetic force networks. No matter where the reference mass may be located in the OPU, concentric positive gravity prevails.

Referring back to Figure 4f, if we imagine the blue mass to be the equivalent of Newton's apple and the apple was in outer space, with no velocity and well away from Earth's influence, it would remain motionless surrounded by MFLs. If another apple were to be placed

24

close to the first apple, with neither having velocity, their proximity would mean that each apple would still be surrounded by MFLs, but for the LFL between them. The LFL would immediately disperse to merge into the MFL network, where the apples would be pushed together.

As to how strong the gravity is must be subject to the overall mass of bodies or planets involved.

Mass Falling to Earth

Figure 5g shows how MFLs relate to a mass "falling to Earth". Note how only vertical force lines are shown, as opposed to all of the MFL

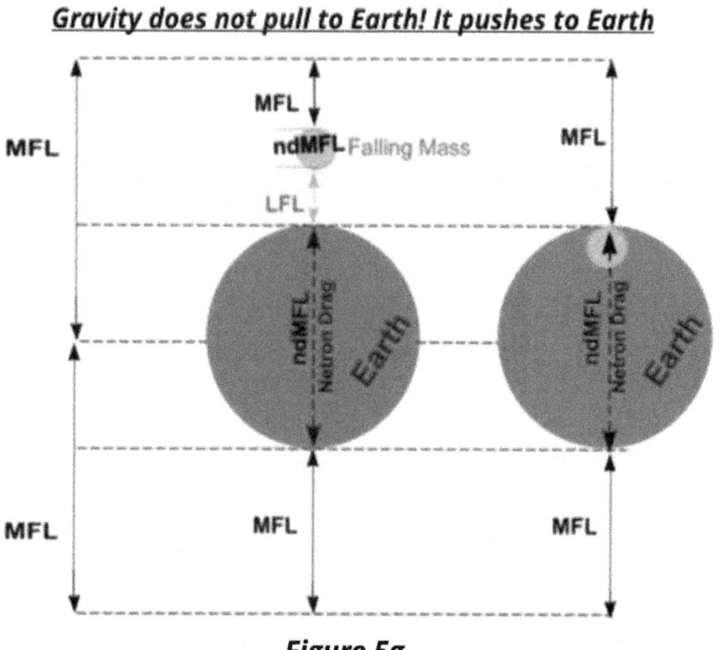

Figure 5g

concentric force lines. That is because other than the relevant unequal pairs of vertical force lines, the remainder of the concentric MFLs are equal. To keep it simple I show only the relevant in-line vertical force lines. The extreme left shows how two counterbalanced MFLs are fundamentally equal. Figure 5g's central configuration shows planet Earth with a "falling mass". The MFLs have been reduced by in-line ndMFLs both in Earth, and in the falling mass with an LFL between them. Because the LFL displaces, to be absorbed by the upper MFL pushing down on the mass, the mass is **pushed** to Earth to become as one with the Earth as shown in the right-hand side of Figure 5g. Perhaps the reader will recognise why the words "falling mass" had inverted commas and the word "pushed" was highlighted in italics!

MFLs Compression (Gravity) on Earth and Moon

Figure 5h is of a similar configuration applied to the Earth and Moon, where the MFLs are tending to push the Moon and Earth together. However, because the Moon is flying through space, at 3,683 km/hr, on a directional course that should carry it past Earth, it fails to do so because of the bias of the ndMFLs. Through each degree of orbit, the dividing LFL is replaced by another LFL.

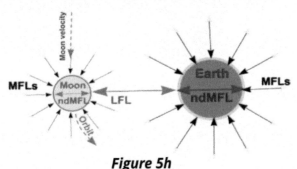

MFLs compression (Gravity) on Earth & Moon

Figure 5h

Where Newton's $9.81m/s^2$ accelerating rate of falling occurs anywhere around Earth, because the Moon is considerably smaller with fewer neutrons than Earth, it has fewer ndMFLs. Therefore, its gravity is considerably less than that of Earth's. This was seen when astronauts walked on the moon, like they were almost floating and were able to make giant leaps without coming to any harm. *Unfortunately, Newton had no idea that the apple was being concentrically pushed from all directions and fell because the LFL between it and Earth immediately dispersed, to become part of the downward pushing MFL, with the ndMFLs in Earth submitting, causing the apple to be pushed to earth.*

As a summation of all my figures leading up to gravity, I show a Structural Schematic of Gravity, titled "Gravity's Elemental Structure, With No Strings Attached" (overleaf).

Gravity's Elemental Structure With No Strings Attached

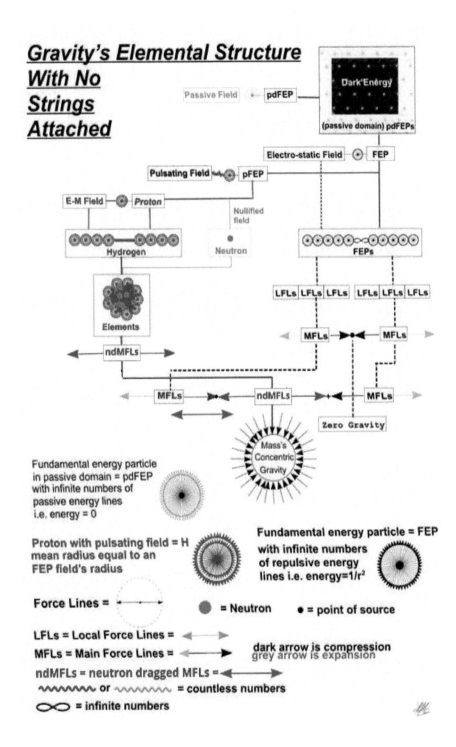

Black Hole

Now, with my derived theory of what part neutrons play in the structures of the OPU and how gravity is in fact concentric all around us, this brings me to how Black Holes are formed.

Figure 6

Figure 6 is the recognised image for a black hole, which is understood to exist at the heart of every galaxy in the OPU.

Please note in the following discussions, where the term MFL is used, it is most likely to be referring to a combination of MFLs and their subordinate LFLs.

Figure 6a illustrates what happens to a neutron if it is denied total concentric MFL containment. It becomes subjected to accelerating spiralling, sending it towards infinite gravity.

The Reversion of a Neutron back to its Fieldless FEP

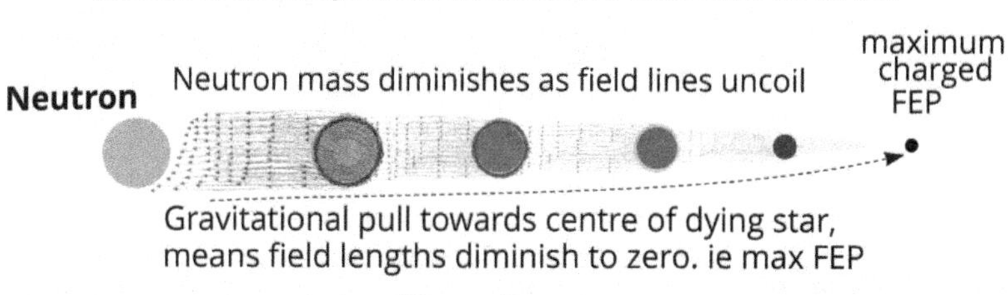

Neutron   Neutron mass diminishes as field lines uncoil   maximum charged FEP

Gravitational pull towards centre of dying star, means field lengths diminish to zero. ie max FEP

Figure 6a

The neutrons, although initially non-repulsive, become caught up in the spiralling of the hydrogen atoms, where their inter-spaced presence enables the hydrogen jiggling and jiving to cease, where resonance forms a definite spiral.

So how do the spiralling conditions evolve in a neutron star?

It was established how pairs of aligned opposing MFLs are always equal in magnitude, giving concentric stabilised zero gravity spherical containment. Even although a neutron star contains a predominant number of neutrons with a lesser amount of H atoms, it's outer spherical force containment by the MFLs is transmitted as a concentric force towards the centre of the volumetric mass, within which its centre becomes predominantly occupied by the lesser numbers of H atoms. The H atoms in their repulsive erratic nature begin to form numerous rogue spirals, which become separate funnels of energy all entrained towards the centre of the neutron star.

Ultimately, the rogue funnels converge into two major funnels diametrically opposite from each other. Although diametrically opposite, their force lines are in no way in opposition to each other, as they both

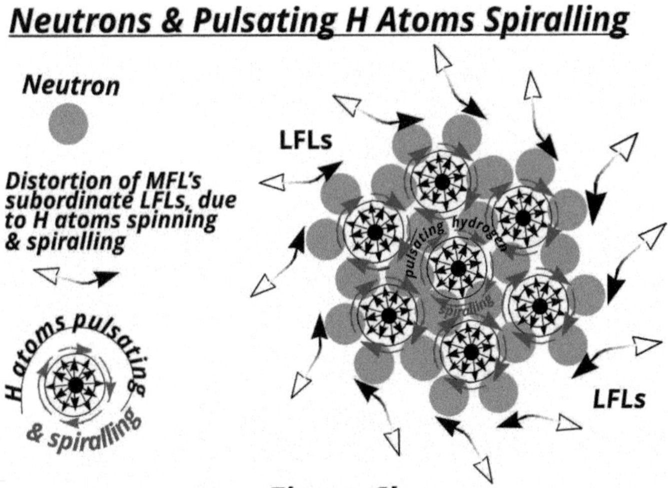

Neutrons & Pulsating H Atoms Spiralling

Neutron

Distortion of MFL's subordinate LFLs, due to H atoms spinning & spiralling

H atoms pulsating & spiralling

LFLs

pulsating hydrogen spiralling

LFLs

Figure 6b

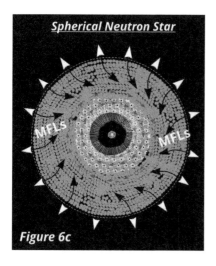

Spherical Neutron Star

Figure 6c

have the same rotation relative to the star's central point.

The H atoms, together with their surrounding neutrons, as in Figure 6b, in their spiralling state, gravitate towards the centre of the star which has begun forming the black infinite gravity zone.

With reference to Figure 6c, as the spiral diminishes in volume with infinite gravity, the accelerating atoms and neutrons, no longer with concentric containment, undergo transformation, converting into field-less FEPs. The FEPs instantaneously eject out of what has become an expanding black hole, back in to both the OPU's dark and electromagnetic energy particles, to be absorbed once more into what the neighbourhood dictates.

As more and more of the atoms and neutrons are consumed by the infinite gravitational dark energy process, the ultimate death of the star is when the spherical volume diminishes, as in Figure 6d, to firstly become a flat disc format before ultimately transforming into what is recognised as a black hole with a horizon threshold functioning from either side.

Where I have defined the dying neutron star process transforming into a black hole, I feel I should now endeavour to illustrate in an alternative and more detailed format what I have just briefly described.

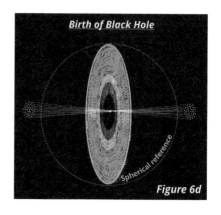

Birth of Black Hole

Figure 6d

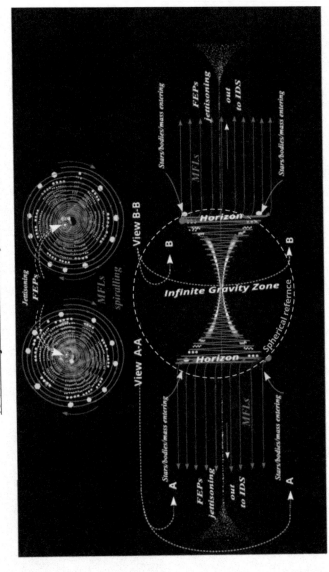

Black Hole Resulting From Mis-aligned Force Lines Spiralling In To Centre of Neutron Star's Infinite Gravity Zone

Figure 6e

Figure 6e shows the situation where ultimately a neutron star, having ceased to be spherical, has two **sets** of opposing MFLs which **do not meet in direct opposition**, owing to their spiralling being of the same rotation. Together, both spirals form an infinite gravity zone and two horizons, where all that enters them under-go a non-reversible, element dismantling process. Figure 6e illustrates the elongated instantaneous process for us to see what is happening in the double horizon void.

Note that the white arrow heads A-A and B-B show the directional views of each of the MFL spirals, where A-A is a view into the A-A spiral, B-B is viewed in the same direction, where one looks through the infinite gravity core, and out through the 2nd horizon.

With infinite gravity, of course, all that enters a black hole horizon is entering so fast that not even light can escape. All matter, entering either horizon no longer with 360° MFL containment, immediately loses its molecular structure, where all atoms come apart, reverting, initially, to their hydrogen and neutron components, before their individual energy fields elongate linearly, as illustrated for a helium atom in Figure 6f.

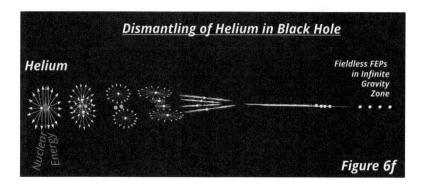

Dismantling of Helium in Black Hole

Helium

Fieldless FEPs in Infinite Gravity Zone

Nuclear Energy

Figure 6f

It shows how, with no concentric gravity, the helium atom comes apart, separating its two hydrogen atoms and two neutrons. Note how each neutron reverts to being of an atom formation. The atoms, in accelerating towards the infinite gravity zone, causes their fields to elongate. The stretched fields diminish back into their maximum energy mass to enter the infinite gravity zone as field-less FEPs in an instant of cool process. The field-less FEPs travel faster than the speed of light, out through the centre of the opposing spiralling cone. In their jettisoning out, back into the OPU, their departing velocity together with its massive deceleration causes the FEPs' temperature to increase, where they glow as fountains of energy.

I once again emphasise that the process is so rapid that the elongation, graphically drawn, is purely to enable the understanding of what does happen in an instant, when elongation occurs. That does not actually exist in normal time scales and is of course invisible within the horizon.

Figure 6g is my attempt to illustrate how the phenomenal *infinite gravity zone (IGZ)* receives the continuous stream of reverted

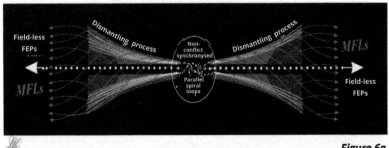

Expanded View of Infinite Gravity Zone

Figure 6g

FEPs entering from both directions in mutual synchronous spirals. Where the black hole's spiralling MFL network regulates the flow of disseminating mass into the IGZ as FEPs, I have tried to convey what must be *non-conflicting synchronised parallel spiral loops (NCSPPLs)* of FEP flows, which, instead of meeting head-on, flow in parallel spirals, until they are ejected as streams of glowing energy points out into the IDS, as shown previously in Figure 6e. By virtue of

FEPs' Synchronised,Non-Conflicing, Parallel, Spiralling Looped Routes

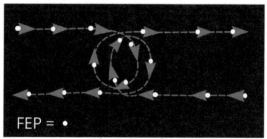

FEP = •

Figure 6h

their positive polarity, they repulse each other where they separate evenly, each 50%, ejecting freely out in their respective directions, through the two phenomenal central tunnels, formed by the infinite gravity framed by the horizon.

Figure 6h is a simplified illustration of the NCSPPL process, where maximum charged repulsive FEPs travelling "faster" than the speed of light, flow momentarily in the same spiralling direction, before shooting out at unimaginably retarding velocity in either of the two directions available to them. The figure in its simplicity shows the two streams of FEPs to be as if remaining in their own through-route.

I am of the opinion that the infinite gravity zone synchronises all transiting FEPs. In their synchrony, they will eject in either direction, i.e. some, actually leaving, through the core of the vortex they came in by. This is a subject best left to professional physicists to give mathematical verification to what I am theorising! Bearing in mind that all that occurs in a black hole, occurs so fast that as well as light appearing to be non-existent, so too is time and distance. It would be as if none of it is happening, were it not for the two decelerating jets of energy discharging, primarily as *field-less FEPs,* instantly re-expanding their field lines as they seek universal balance once more.

Their repulsion causes them to fly apart from each other to ultimately decelerate and unite singularly with a random group of twelve FEPs, to once more become a central FEP in a formation of thirteen, as described in Figure 3. Having once more extended their electrostatic energy field-lines, their expansion enables them to environmentally adjust to their new-found locations. Because of their rate of expansion, in their new locations they will erratically pulsate to be transformed back into electromagnetic pulsating energy. Thus, with all the numbers of re-formed field-less FEPs restoring the population of compressed particles, the IDS's expansive state is maintained.

Where one hears so much about the "various forces" said to exist and incorporated in string theory, I believe any force variations must stem from:

1) *The electrostatic force of the FEP*
2) *The electromagnetic force of hydrogen and all mass*

Gravity is the difference between 1 and 2, due the presence of neutrons.

Surely, the electrostatic force is the mystical singularity, where all that becomes subject to concentric compression converts to pulsating mass forming and life-giving energy!

Starlight

In view of how I arrived at my theory on gravity, I choose to pose the following concept along the same lines. I believe the photos taken of my window-sill as the sun rays' angle changed across the glass ornament, showing separately the four primary colours, each radiating their respective fragmented, non-continuous light "beams". The images show the "beams" to comprise of minute ray-bits of energy surges, emanating through the element structure of the room's atmosphere. They do appear to confirm the particle structure of our OPU. Of course, the particle structure in the

Sunlight through multi-facetted glass showing broken ray line colours

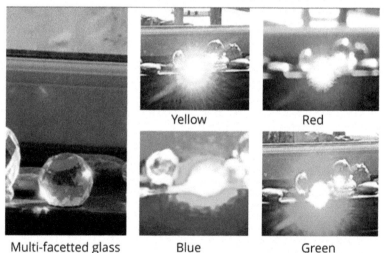

Multi-facetted glass   Yellow   Red

                              Blue   Green

photographs cannot be that of FEPs, but must surely be a result of light's electromagnetic inductive transmission through the atmosphere's element structure.

Where pFEPs were first defined, they were given as being totally passive. It was also given that the FEP's charge is subject to its location. Thus, as Figure 3 showed, groupings of 13 have domain field volumes where their repulsion balances with its neighbours. Verging into the realms of conjecture, I ask the reader to consider the following.

The FEP volumes being expansive means the weak to passive regions of their fields overlap with their neighbours, as shown in Figure7. Where passivity can be a total status throughout a pFEP, it can also be a part condition for an FEP or atom, since its electrostatic potential varies from maximum charge through to weak, weaker and passive. Where the neighbourhood dictates the measure of repulsive charge, in its balanced repulsive structure, it does not restrict the weak to passive strength pulsations from occurring throughout the passive and non-passive zones of the FEP or atoms' fields. Note how I show each successive FEP's induced pulse of light energy to be 90° out of step with its upstream neighbour's, weak to passive field volume.

Thus, we have the electromagnetically induced transmissions of

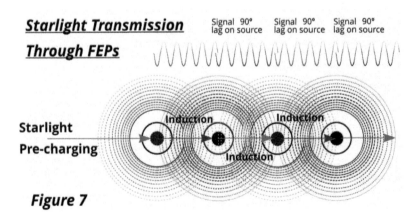

Figure 7

light passing throughout all neighbourhoods of the OPU as if light-beams, which are in effect chain reactions of light energy transmitting from one FEP or atom to its twelve surrounding neighbours. The transmitting fragmentations of light are illustrated on the glass ornament photographs shown earlier.

Whether FEPs or atoms, Figure 8 shows how, *tangentially*, they each emulate a star radiating its light in six (twelve, three dimensionally) respective directions.

With reference to the extreme left nucleus, I superimpose a pulsating charge, shown strong red, indicating direction of radiation on the over-lapping, weak to passive region of the field. That pulsation or signal instantly induces a light energy pulsation to the next FEP or H atom, which instantly radiates in every direction. The signal varies in strength depending on which direction it is radiating. The induced signal is strongest when directly aligned with its light source.

Light Radiation by Induction across Neighbourhood Group of FEPs or Atoms

Any non-aligned light signals will reinforce or diminish light from a star or other tangential light source transmissions.

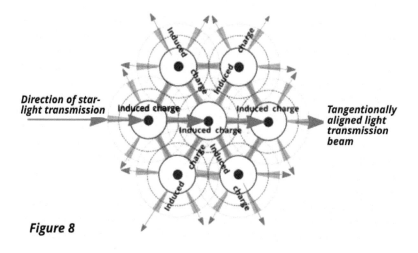

Direction of star-light transmission

Tangentionally aligned light transmission beam

Figure 8

Einstein suggested that star-light bends around the sun. Perhaps these few pages will throw a "different light" on the historical belief that starlight travels in continuous straight beams of energy. My approach I believe explains how it truly is. The mode of transmission, would explain Einstein's theory of starlight beams appearing to bend around the sun.

This is a subject worthy of a paper, alone!

The Dual Slot
Baffle Transmission Chamber

In view of my rejection of the electron concept, and how I relate all energy-change or fluctuations to be functions of electromagnetic force networks, ultimately as these are functions of the dark energy network wherein they occur, one must re-examine the findings adopted by the scientific world over the past century.

Figure 9 shows what the fundamental arrangement of a dual slot baffle chamber comprises of. Where the physics books I have read referred to the transmitter radiating energy waves, I assume they regarded these waves to be the energy the transmitter's positive charge created with its maximum value dropping to minimum level, the instant a discharge occurs. Field lines are drawn to pass through either gap in the baffle, to immediately spread out in repulsion.

That is an approximation of what is actually occurring. With reference to my discussion on LFLs and MFLs, the chamber is of course populated by air atoms, all of which are subject to the relayed pulsations of the transmitter's charge. The atoms provide paths by which the charge is transmitted through the gaps to reach the receptor panel, of course resulting in what seems like beams of energy spreading out. Where countless discharges are occurring in rapid succession, only one discharged white hot spot is occurring at any one instant and can be anywhere on the receiving screen, resulting in the illuminated pattern forming. The multi-lines are a representative compromise of what is actually occurring in the network of force lines

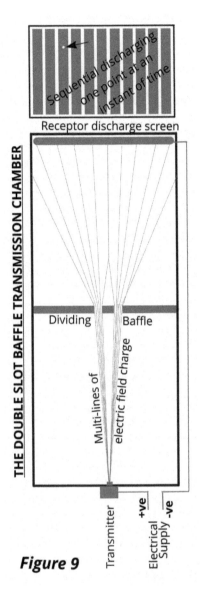

Figure 9

throughout the atmosphere within the chamber.

I emphasise that the discharge is not an electron, free to fly around anywhere as an independent entity or particle. It is a transferal of energy from a high to lower potential. Once it has reached the receiver, the energy has been imparted as short-lived heat or light. *No flying particle exists*.

Where the display comprised of random deflected discharges, ultimately people such as J Logie Baird recognised how to take the randomness out of such energy transmissions by arranging a electromagnetically polarised apperture in place of the slotted barrier. *Thus, by energising the transmitter with the varying potential signal of a movie recording, the film's high frequency discharges, striking the receptor screen to form the moving picture, television was born.*

Magnet

If my theory of how neutrons form stands, might I suggest that the same principle be applied to the structure of the molten iron in the heart of planet Earth. Surely, the iron's fluidised metal, in motion due to Earth's rotation, means distortion of the iron atoms' energy fields. I therefore present Figures 10, 10a, 10b and10c.

Figure 10, represents an iron atom with its field's force lines shown from full strength all equally radiating *out towards passivity*. Whether it is one FEP or one multi-nuclei iron atom, the ultimate 360° field radiation must exist.

Figure 10a illustrates how an iron atom's field varying in lava flow, has nigh on 90% of its field radiate out at angles ranging from 80° to 60°, where it buckles against the direction of lava flow. In buckling the field lines extend towards passivity to become common with the in line extended trailing field lines.

Such a situation of course does not exist, as molten iron atom lava flow comprises of infinite numbers of atoms forming parallel lines of energised series of atoms.

Static iron atom with monopole force lines strong to passive

Figure 10

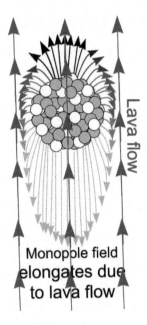

Figure 10a

Such series relate as Figure 10b shows. Note how the leading atom's trailing field lines don't just buckle but double back on themselves due to the oncoming atom's maximum strength field lines. The result is for the double backed force lines to become merged with the maximum force lines.

As this is occurring in not just two, but in the whole series

Magnet Formation in Earth's Molten Lava Core

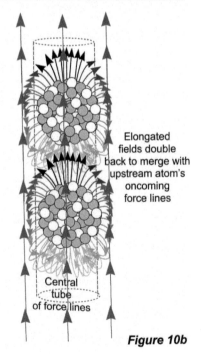

Figure 10b

of atoms, the combined maximum and double backed force lines in effect form a central tube of force lines, where the ultimate leading atom projects maximum repulsion, and the ultimate lagging atom has an attractive force. Thus, when an identical pair is brought in line with the first pair, they are immediately attracted to each other to form what is in fact a magnet.

As Figure 10c illustrates, whether it is a small cluster

of iron atoms or an iron bar, straight or horseshoe, it is a magnet with north and south poles. Ideally this subject requires mathematics to verify this possible phenomenon, which I must leave to someone more versed in such physics.

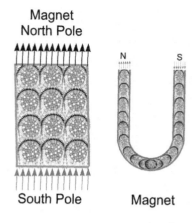

Figure 10c

Conclusion

I suspect because of magnetism and Earth's North and South Poles, what the scientific fraternity, such as Faraday with his electromagnetic induction work gave the world, *somehow monopole charges alone, seemed irrelevant to academia and the industrial society and have consequently been ignored.*

I hope my concept will change this and it will be recognised that the BDEO's expansive tendency of its electrostatic passive charged points (particles), is surely where singularity lies. The instant an electrostatic charge is subjected *not to a reversal of polarity*, but merely the pulsating transience of the positive charge of a monopole energy point, then such pulsations brought on by variations in its field volume become electromagnetic and remain so, either as an H atom, a neutron or combined masses of both until they pass through a Black Hole as electrostatic FEPs once more.

In short, surely, with electromagnetism resulting from the retarded expansion (compression) of monopole points of positive fields, therein lies the ultimate SINGULARITY from which all is evolved.

The adverse reports we are seeing on current news bulletins, initially inspired by Sir David Attenborough's roll in raising awareness of the clearly negative changes to our global climate, with the melting ice caps and Australia's forest fires spreading over vast areas of the continent, there is plenty of evidence of what is before us.

My theory, explaining gravity as it truly is, has to be accepted by academia and industry. We must immediately set out to gradually replace combustion engines, rockets, and jets with their exhaust gases needlessly polluting Earth's atmosphere. Clean anti-gravity lift-off flight with more efficient electric power-driven modes will be perfected, using such as Sandy Kidd's dual gyro concept.

The historically near-priceless, "gravitational static heads of mountain reservoirs" hydro-electric power generation can once more be given its true place in society's needs, together with the Sun's heat energy harnessed by solar panels. With the true understanding of gravity, surely our capitalist system can be re-channelled into conforming to Nature's life-giving needs. We should not just turn away from producing non-reversible plastics but recognise that it is the chemical industry's responsibility to clear the waste up and provide reversible plastics, or other nature-conforming materials.

Where I have listed the books that I have read, I am disappointed I found that no one challenged the general acceptance of the electrons "apparent presence" in the compilation of their work. Of all the books listed, I find Lee Smolin's "inverted titled" book *The Trouble with Physics* informative, refreshingly frank and possibly reassuring for my daring to put forward my personal theorising on gravity and singularity.

Finally, Carlo Rovelli's book *Reality is Not What It Seems* was similarly informative, which is why I have drawn my "Gravity's Elemental Structure With no Strings Attached" along the same lines as his page 65's *Fig 3.5 titled* "What The World is Made Of".

As I enter the list of authors' work I have read, I am including the late Michael Talbot's book, "Mysticism & The New Physics". I am reminded of how he endeavoured to link ancient mystical philosophies with modern physics to justify how such ancient beliefs could be valid. Had he been alive today, he might have recognised concentric gravity to be the link he was seeking.

As an engineer, I recall not allowing my thoughts to ponder too much on what Talbot claimed to have experienced, as I was too involved with my real concern, solving of modern-day public and industrial service plant operational problems. It could be that in recognising the true fabric of the Universe to be along the lines of what my book describes, perhaps those who advocate the concept of Universal Consciousness will recognise that concentric gravity is wherein it lies.

Finally, I recall when I was a teenager, how our family doctor, together with a local church minister, had cause to attended a young Irish girl who, whilst living with her aunt in the nearby village of Sauchie, was sent home from school, due to disturbances in the classroom. It is on record that when she was in class, books and papers would fly around the classroom. The teacher very soon recognised that it only happened when the girl was present. Our doctor and the minister both sat by the child's bed while she slept. They witnessed her sleeping body, levitating above the bed. Apparently the mysterious occurrences ceased when she was returned to her family in Ireland.

Could it be that the concentric gravity we all have acting on our individual body's elemental repulsion forces, in some way became distorted around the girl? If her inherent repulsion forces were abnormally turbulent, through subconscious distress, perhaps they brought about an even stronger imbalance than that experienced by the afore-mentioned Sandy Kidd with the "live" gyroscope in his pocket.

I hope that the last two anecdotes do not diminish the readers' interest, and that what I propose relative to gravity, singularity, magnetism, Black Holes and light transmission "sparks" the imagination of academia.

I REST MY CASE

References

Authors	Book Titles	Year Published
Brian Cox & Jeff Forshaw	The Quantum Physics: Everything That Can Happen Does.	2012
Carlo Rovelli	Seven Brief Lesson in Physics	2012
Carlo Rovelli	Reality is Not hat it Seems	2016
Frank Close	Antimatter	2010
Jeff Stewart	Why Balloons Rise and Apples Fall	2017
Joanne Baker	50 Quantum Physics Ideas: You Really Should Know	2013
Laurence M Krauss	A Universe From Nothing: Why There is Something	2012
Lee Smolin	The Trouble With Physics	2008
Lee Smolin	Einstein's Unfinished Revolution	2019
Michio Kaku	Hyperspace: A Scientific Odyssey Through the Tenth Dimension	1999
Michio Kaku	Parallel Worlds: Science of the Alternative Universe and Ours	2006
Michael Talbot	Mysticism and The New Physics	1993
New Scientist	Nothing: From Absolute Zero to Cosmic Oblivion – Amazing Insight to Nothingness	2013
Nigel Calder	Magic Universe: A Grand Tour of Modern Science	2005
Richard Panek	The 4% Universe: Dark Matter Dark Energy and The Race To Discover the Rest of Reality	2010
Robert P Crease	The Great Equations: The Hunt For Cosmic Beauty	2009
Sean Carroll	The Particle at the End of The Universe	2013
Stephen Hawking	The Essential Einstein: His Greatest Works	2008
Multi Contributors	The Science Book	2015

(John Farndon, Dan Green, Derek Harvey, Penny Johnson, Douglas Palmer, Steve Parker, Giles Sparrow)

Authors	Magazine	Year published
Multi Contributors	Scientific American – Extreme Physics	2019
Multi Contributors	Scientific & Medical Network – Paradigm Explorer	2019